A TEACHER'S LOVE

In loving memory of my father. Thank you for showing me that through education, anything is possible. You will forever be part of my journey.

ISBN 979-8-9850363-0-5

A TEACHER'S LOVE

WORDS BY
LISA WILLS

PICTURES BY
GEORGE SWEETLAND

Reasons I love My Teacher
1. Believes in Me
2. Makes learning fun
3. Teaches me about math and animals
4. Dance Parties
5. She knows my family
6. Teaches me about life

When I go to school, I know I will feel loved. I will feel special.

I know that I matter because my teacher shows me that she cares.

Some days, things are tough at home.
When I come to school, it's hard to
concentrate.

Hard days at home make school days really rough.

During those tough times, my teacher always reminds me that I can accomplish anything I put my mind to!

I am understood! She knows all about my family.
My teacher calls my mom and dad all the time.

She brags on my behavior and she discusses my grades. I will also get a call if I misbehave.

He's working hard!

He's a role model!

He never gives up!

WORD WALL

Resilience Perseverance Respect

Self-Control Integrity Collaboration

Critical-Thinking Empathy

My teacher is fun! She taught me how to do many things!

DO YOU KNOW YOUR FACTS?

DANCE PARTY LESSON

I learned to love animals.

I see the beauty in all insects.

I have been shown how to respect myself and all the people around me.

I even learned how
to do yoga poses
and cut flowers.

When my school work is hard, I don't give up!

My teacher tells me to keep my head held high and give the task another try.

When a mistake is made, I can always correct my mistake and make things right.

I also learned that asking for help is okay. When I ask questions I understand better.

Asking questions is part of learning, a part of life.

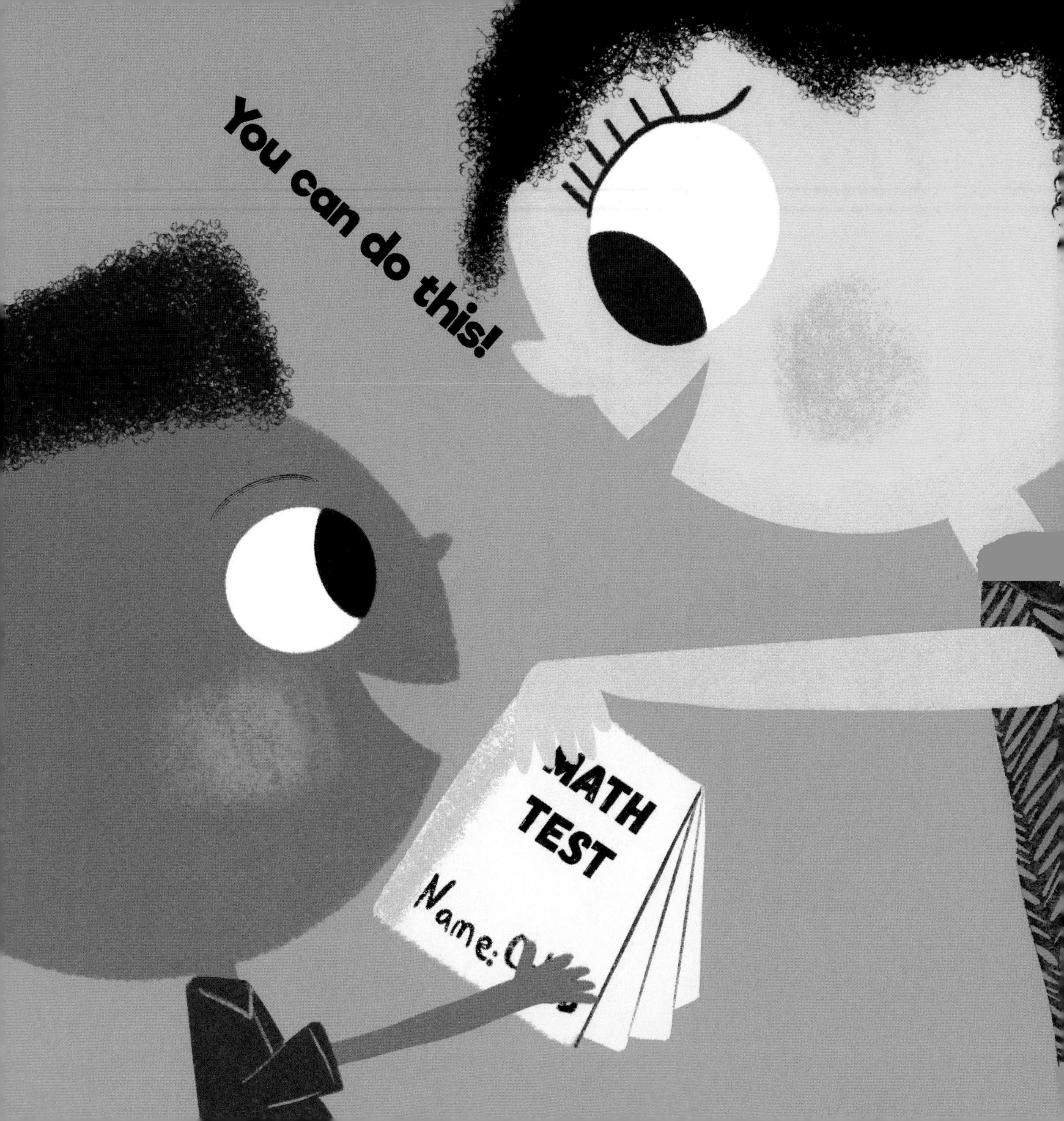
You can do this!
MATH TEST
Name:

My teacher believes in me, she shows me every day!

Her hugs make me feel special.
I can feel love through my teacher's embrace.

LEADERSHIP

TECHNOLOGY

SERVICE TO COMMUNITY

EDUCATION

GOVERNMENT

She has shown me that the world is a very big place, with lots of opportunities!

Now I dream big and work hard towards my goals. If I work hard enough, one day my dreams will come true!

What will I grow up
and do?

Dear Mrs. Wills,
Thank you for
teaching me math
I am grateful
for every thing.

Mrs. Wills,
you are a like
mother figure to
me Mrs. Wills

Thank you for
loving me and
teaching me about
life.

Mrs. Wills
Thank you for
loving me.

Thank you for
Teaching me
multiplication
Mrs. Wills

I LOVE
YOU
Mrs. Wills

Mrs Wills I love the way you teach.

Thank you for making class so fun we love you Mrs. Wills I had alot of fun in your class and helped alot I love math

We love you Mrs. Wills you are the best teacher ever and I love you.

Thank you for helping me with my attitude you are loved.

I am confident and happy! Thank you mrs. Wills!

Mrs. Wills you make math fun!

Made in the USA
Monee, IL
13 December 2022